ELLIE GOULDING

LIGHTS

WISE PUBLICATIONS
PART OF THE MUSIC SALES GROUP
LONDON / NEW YORK / PARIS / SYDNEY / COPENHAGEN / BERLIN / MADRID / HONG KONG / TOKYO

PUBLISHED BY
WISE PUBLICATIONS
14/15 BERNERS STREET, LONDON WIT 3LJ, UK.

EXCLUSIVE DISTRIBUTORS:
MUSIC SALES LIMITED
DISTRIBUTION CENTRE, NEWMARKET ROAD,
BURY ST EDMUNDS, SUFFOLK IP33 3YB, UK.

MUSIC SALES PTY LIMITED
20 RESOLUTION DRIVE, CARINGBAH, NSW 2229, AUSTRALIA.

ORDER NO. AM1000516
ISBN 978-1-84938-527-5

MUSIC ARRANGED BY VASCO HEXEL AND DEREK JONES.
MUSIC PROCESSED BY PAUL EWERS MUSIC DESIGN.

PRINTED IN THE EU.

WWW.MUSICSALES.COM

YOUR GUARANTEE OF QUALITY:
AS PUBLISHERS, WE STRIVE TO PRODUCE EVERY BOOK
TO THE HIGHEST COMMERCIAL STANDARDS.

THE MUSIC HAS BEEN FRESHLY ENGRAVED AND THE BOOK HAS BEEN
CAREFULLY DESIGNED TO MINIMISE AWKWARD PAGE TURNS AND TO MAKE
PLAYING FROM IT A REAL PLEASURE. PARTICULAR CARE HAS BEEN GIVEN
TO SPECIFYING ACID-FREE, NEUTRAL-SIZED PAPER MADE FROM PULPS
WHICH HAVE NOT BEEN ELEMENTAL CHLORINE BLEACHED.

THIS PULP IS FROM FARMED SUSTAINABLE FORESTS AND
WAS PRODUCED WITH SPECIAL REGARD FOR THE ENVIRONMENT.

THROUGHOUT, THE PRINTING AND BINDING HAVE BEEN PLANNED
TO ENSURE A STURDY, ATTRACTIVE PUBLICATION WHICH SHOULD GIVE
YEARS OF ENJOYMENT.

IF YOUR COPY FAILS TO MEET OUR HIGH STANDARDS, PLEASE INFORM US
AND WE WILL GLADLY REPLACE IT.

GUNS AND HORSES

WORDS & MUSIC BY ELLIE GOULDING & JOHN FORTIS

5

- pen,   heav - en___ knows___   you're so___   worth___ it,___   you_____

are.___

But I wish I__ could_

___ feel_____ it   all_____ for_____ you.   I wish I___could

be_____ it   all   for_____ you.___   If I could__ e -

6

STARRY EYED

WORDS & MUSIC BY ELLIE GOULDING & JONNY LATTIMER

14

THIS LOVE (WILL BE YOUR DOWNFALL)

WORDS & MUSIC BY ELLIE GOULDING & FIN DOW-SMITH

1. Who are we to be e-mo-tion-al?
2. Who are you to make me feel so good?
(love.)

19

20

23

UNDER THE SHEETS

WORDS & MUSIC BY ELLIE GOULDING & FIN DOW-SMITH

like all the boys be-fore, like all the boys be-fore.__ This is our luck,__ ba - by, run-ning out. Our clothes were nev - er off.__ We still have our__ roads to run a - bout. To scale the map, to scale the map to get us back on__ track.

26

29

THE WRITER

WORDS & MUSIC BY ELLIE GOULDING & JONNY LATTIMER

34

EVERY TIME YOU GO

WORDS & MUSIC BY ELLIE GOULDING, JOHN FORTIS & FIN DOW-SMITH

2, 3.

Maybe we forgot all the things we are, we are to-
Do you know the price I paid for all the times I saved? We were to-

-geth - er.
-geth - er.

1° only
N.C.

Wake me up, wake me up.

Stop my fall. (Ev - ry - time you

41

42

44

WISH I STAYED

WORDS & MUSIC BY ELLIE GOULDING

49

51

YOUR BIGGEST MISTAKE

WORDS & MUSIC BY ELLIE GOULDING & FRASER T. SMITH

1. Take cov - er. Signs don't show.

You drove me off the road. But

I'LL HOLD MY BREATH

WORDS & MUSIC BY ELLIE GOULDING & FIN DOW-SMITH

60

SALT SKIN

WORDS & MUSIC BY ELLIE GOULDING & FIN DOW-SMITH

1. You're as

72

LIGHTS

WORDS & MUSIC BY ELLIE GOULDING,
RICHARD STANNARD & ASH HOWE

Lights,   lights,   lights,   l - l - l - lights.

Lights,   lights,   lights,   lights,   lights,   lights,